Millions of photographs and billions of words have been printed on Ireland's landscape, her plant life and her inland waters, yet the magnificence of the marine life around her coast equals, if not surpasses, that terrestrial beauty.

We at Sherkin Island Marine Station, since our foundation in 1975, have in our own small way attempted to introduce people to these marine wonders with our research and educational programmes, conferences, exhibitions and various publications. However in those 17 years we have always wanted to do true justice to that world of beauty with a photographic book such as this.

The photographs are the work of a brilliant photographer, Paul Kay, who spent many hours dedicated to capturing the perfect shot. His work speaks for itself.

The photographs chosen give but a glimpse of the thousands of animals and plants in Ireland's coastal waters. We hope that they will give people a new awareness of Ireland's wonderful Natural Resource - the Sea.

We would like to thank sincerely the following sponsors for the generous support we received for the book:

Cork Examiner Publications Ltd.
Cork Harbour Commissioners
Dept. of the Environment
Eli Lilly S.A.
National Parks & Wildlife Service of the Office of Public Works
Penn Chemicals - SmithKline Beecham
Pfizer Pharmaceuticals
Salmara Fisheries Ltd.
Schering-Plough (Brinny)
Údarás na Gaeltachta

"We only see a little of the ocean,
A few miles distance from the rocky shore;
But oh! out there beyond - beyond the eyes' horizon
There's more - there's more."

*This book is dedicated to the memory of Eileen.*

*A wonderful wife, mother and friend.*

# FOREWORD

For those of us who love the sea, this book will become a treasured possession, illuminating as it does in a most vibrant way the magnificence of the marine life, around our coasts.

Sherkin Island Marine Station has developed over the years, from small beginnings, to become a most important depository of marine data. It has made, and is continuing to make, a major contribution to our understanding of the flora and fauna of our coastal areas.

It is vital that the diversity of our marine life be maintained for its own intrinsic value and for the benefit of present and future generations. I believe that this book will imbue all with a sense of pride and wonder, at the richness of our environment and with a strong desire to protect it.

I congratulate all involved in Sherkin Island Marine Station on their magnificent work.

NOEL TREACY, T.D.,
Minister for Heritage Affairs and Wildlife at The Office of Public Works.
September, 1992.

Published by SHERKIN ISLAND MARINE STATION PUBLICATIONS
First published November 1992

British Library Cataloguing-in-Publication Data.
A catalogue record for this book is available from the British Library.

ISBN: 1 870492 75 7


Design & typesetting: Susan Murphy, Sherkin Island Marine Station, Co. Cork, Ireland
Colour Separations by: Litho Studios, Dublin, Ireland
Printed by: City Printing Works Ltd., Victoria Cross, Cork, Ireland
Binding by: Future Print, Dublin & Library Binding, Dublin, Ireland

## ACKNOWLEDGEMENTS

Sherkin Island Marine Station would like to acknowledge the assistance of a number of people who made a special contribution to this book.

To the biologists at the marine station, in particular Timothy Budd, Richard Hatch, Chris Pater, Donal Thorp and Amanda Wilkinson.  To Michael and Robbie Murphy who were boatmen to the various diving locations. To Dr. Gillian Bishop who helped with identification of the various species.

Thanks to Michael Herley; Denis MacSweeney, Photographic Shop, Cork; and Noel and Ciaran Dunlea, Paper Sales Ltd., Cork, for the help they gave.

A small number of photographs were taken by people who previously visited Sherkin Island Marine Station. Their photographs have been acknowledged.

Is mian leis na foilsitheoirí a mbuíochas a ghabháil leis an mBuanchoiste Téarmaíochta, An Roinn Oideachais, as a gcomhairle agus as an gcabhair a thug siad maidir leis na leaganacha Gaeilge atá sa leabhar seo, agus go háirithe le Colm Breathnach, Rúnaí, agus le Fidelma Ní Ghallchobhair, Rúnaí Taighde.

The publishers wish to thank An Buanchoiste Téarmaíochta (The Permanent Terminology Committee of the Department of Education) for their advice and help with the Irish versions in this book, and especially Colm Breathnach, Secretary, and Fidelma Ní Ghallchobhair, Research Secretary.

The Latin translation for all animal and plant names has been given, and the English and Irish translations when available.  When the Irish translation was not available for a specific species the translation of the species in general was supplied in brackets.

# IRELAND'S MARINE LIFE

## A WORLD of BEAUTY

### EDITORS
Matt Murphy
Susan Murphy

### PHOTOGRAPHER
Paul Kay

A Sherkin Island Marine Station Publication

*Crenilabrus melops* - Corkwing Wrasse - *Bochar*

(Photographer: Paul Kay)

*Actinia equina* - Beadlet Anemone - *Bundún coirníneach*

The beadlet anemone is easy to find on the seashore at low tide,
looking quite like little red blobs of jelly.

(Photographer: Paul Kay)

**Above:** *Labrus mixtus* - Cuckoo Wrasse - *Ballach Muire*

This is one of the most colourful fish to be found around our coasts

(Photographer: Paul Kay)

**Below:** *Bifurcaria bifurcata*

A brown seaweed typical of rock pools.

(Photographer: Paul Kay)

**Left:** *Ophiocomina nigra*
Black Brittle-star

The black brittle-star tends to be bigger then the common brittle-star and is not always black!

(Photographer: Paul Kay)

**Above:** *Zeus Faber* - John Dory

The black dot acts as a defence mechanism. It appears as an eye to other fish, frightening them away. Legend has it that the black spot is the fingerprint of St. Peter.

(Photographer: Paul Kay)

**Opposite page:** *Archidoris pseudoargus*
Sea Lemon
*Bodalach*

(Photographer: Paul Kay)

**Below:** *Gobius paganellus*
Rock Goby
*Mac siobháin carraige*

The rock goby is typically found in pools amongst seaweed.

(Photographer: Paul Kay)

Below & Right:  *Alcyonium digitatum* - Dead Man's Fingers - *Meara mara*

Dead man's fingers are not one animal but a colony of individuals, each of which has a small white retractable polyp.

(Photographer: Paul Kay)

This diver is examining an underwater
seascape.

(Photographer: Paul Brazier)

**Above:** *Galathea strigosa* - Spiny Squat Lobster - *(Gliomach)*

The squat lobster lives in narrow crevices and only emerges at night.

(Photographer: Paul Kay)

**Right:** A spiny squat lobster's face.

(Photographer: Paul Kay)

**Overleaf:** *Bispira volutacornis* - Fan Worm

This fan worm can rapidly retract its feather-like tentacles when disturbed.

(Photographer: Paul Kay)

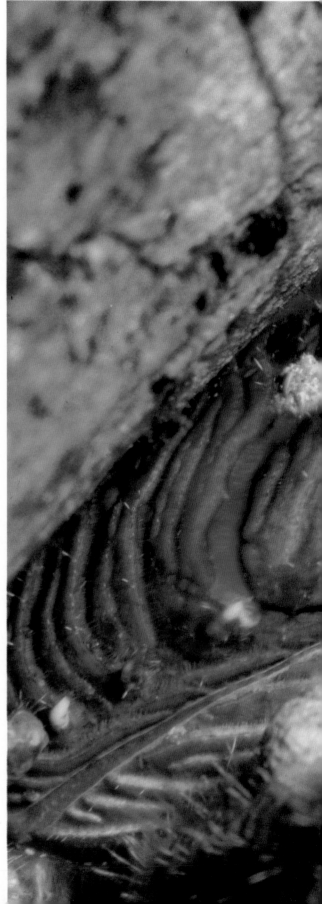

16

*Centrolabrus exoletus* - Rock Cook - *Ballach fuarleice*

(Photographer: Paul Kay)

**Opposite page:** *Bunodactis verrucosa*
Gem Anemone
*(Bundún leice)*

(Photographer: Paul Kay)

**Above:** *Sagartia elegans* var. *nivea*
*(Bundún leice)*

This anemone appears as a white disc with white tentacles.

(Photographer: Paul Kay)

**Left:** *Cereus pedunculatus*
Daisy Anemone
*(Bundún leice)*

(Photographer: Paul Kay)

21

The hermit crab usually inhabits discarded whelk shells.

(Photographer: Paul Kay)

*Galathea intermedia* - Squat Lobster - *Gliomach*

(Photographer: Paul Kay)

**Above:** A flatfish's eye.

(Photographer: Paul Kay)

**Opposite page:** *Inachus dorsettensis*
Scorpion Spider Crab
*(Portán faoilinne)*

The front claws of the spider crab are normally carried folded under its body.

(Photographer: Paul Kay)

**Right:** *Trisopterus luscus*
Bib or Pout
*Troscán stopóige*

Bib generally has characteristic stripes on its body. It is commonly found in shallow water and also among wrecks.

(Photographer: Paul Kay)

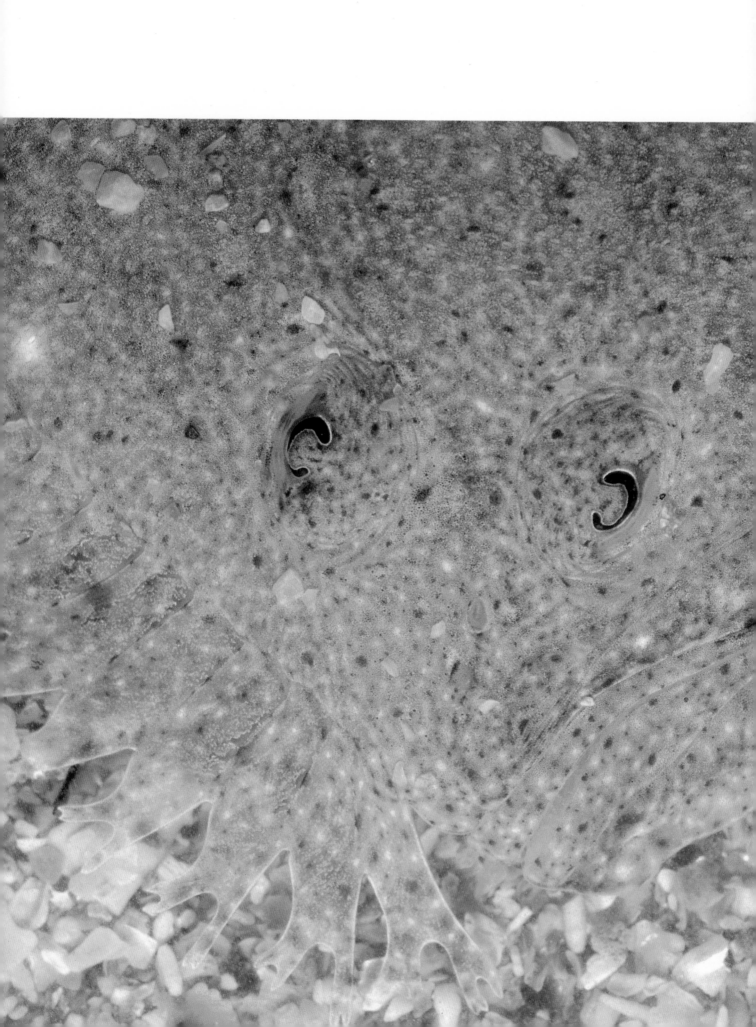

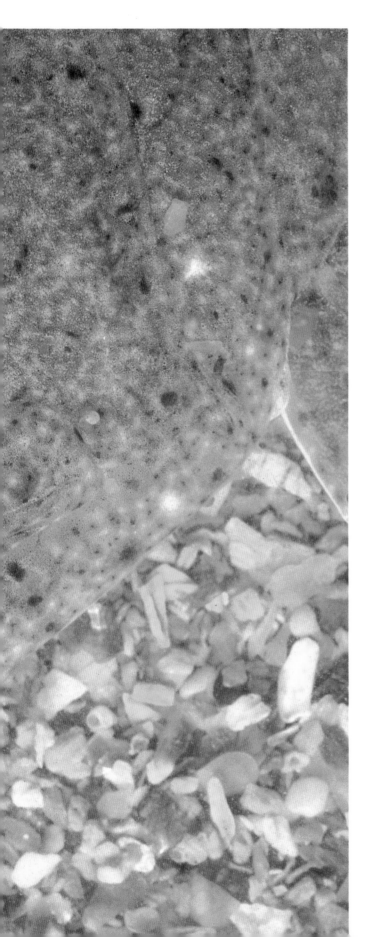

**Above:** Here is a clearer look at the fascinating structure of the brill's head.

(Photographer: Paul Kay)

**Left:** *Scophthalmus rhombus* - Brill - *Broit*

This flatfish is well camouflaged on the sandy seabed.

(Photographer: Paul Kay)

**Above:** *Aspitrigla cuculus* - Red Gurnard - *Cnúdán dearg*

The red gurnard feeds largely on swimming crabs, shrimps and squat lobsters.

(Photographer: Paul Kay)

**Left:** *Anemonia sulcata* - Snakelocks Anemone - *Bundún nathairiúil*

Purple tips are often a characteristic of this anemone.

(Photographer: Paul Kay)

*Palaemon serratus* - Common Prawn - Cloichean

The common prawn is often found in rockpools on the lower shore. Its transparency can make it hard to find in the water.

(Photographer: Paul Kay)

**Above:** *Scyliorhinus canicula*

Lesser-spotted Dogfish

*Fíogach beag*

This is the most well-known member of the shark family occurring in European waters. It has a rough sandpaper-like skin.

(Photographer: Paul Kay)

**Left:** *Scyliorhinus canicula*

Mermaid's Purse

*Púitsín chailleach an tsáile*

Inside the Mermaid's Purse can be seen the developing embryo of the dogfish.

(Photographer: Paul Kay)

**Opposite page:** The egg case is attached to seaweed by a number of tightly wound threads. Empty egg cases can often be seen washed up on beaches.

(Photographer: Paul Kay)

*Pleuronectes platessa* · Plaice · Leathog bhallach
(Photographer: Paul Kay)

*Eupagurus bernhardus* - Common Hermit Crab - *Faocha ghliomaigh*
*Pecten maximus* - Great Scallop - *Muirín*

A hermit crab on a scallop

(Photographer: Ian Watts)

*Patella sp.* - Limpet - Bairneach

*Corallina* algae and young *Chondrus* competing for space on a limpet shell.

(Photographer: Paul Kay)

**Previous page:** *Metridium senile* - Plumose Anemone - *Bláth mara*
(Photographer: Paul Kay)

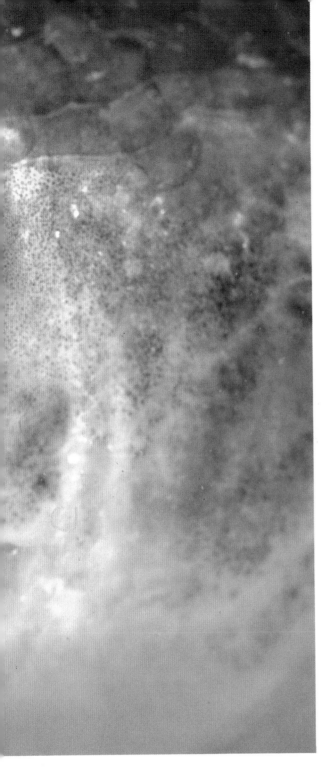

**Left:** *Chelon labrosus* - Thick-lipped Grey Mullet - *Lannach*

This species of mullet can easily be identified by it's large upper lip.

(Photographer: Paul Kay)

**Below:** The thick-lipped grey mullet is commonly found in shallow waters and estuaries.

(Photographer: Paul Kay)

**Above:** *Pecten maximus*
Great Scallop
*Muirín*

This mollusc swims
backwards by opening and
closing the two shells very
quickly.

(Photographer: Paul Kay)

**Left:** The scallop has very basic eyes
which are positioned around the
edge of its shell. These are
used for detecting potential
enemies.

(Photographer: Paul Kay)

**Above:** *Caryophyllia smithii* - Devonshire Cup Coral - *Coiréalach cupach*

This anemone-like creature is in fact a true coral.

(Photographer: Paul Kay)

**Below:** The calcarious cast of the Devonshire cup coral. It has a hard skeleton into which its tentacles can retract.

**Right:** *Eledone cirrhosa*
Lesser Octopus
*An t-ochtapas beag*

The lesser octopus has remarkably good eye-sight. It has the most complex eyes of all invertebrates.

(Photographer: Paul Kay)

**Overleaf:** *Botryllus schlosseri*
Star Sea Squirt
*Ascaid réaltach*

Star Sea Squirt come in a
variety of colours.

(Photographer: Paul Kay)

**Left:** *Halichondria panicea*
Breadcrumb Sponge
*(Spúinse)*

This green sponge has a very characteristic
smell.

(Photographer: Paul Kay)

**Below:** *Archidoris pseudoargus*
Sea Lemon
*(Bodalach)*

This sea slug can usually be found
feeding on breadcrumb sponge.

(Photographer: Paul Kay)

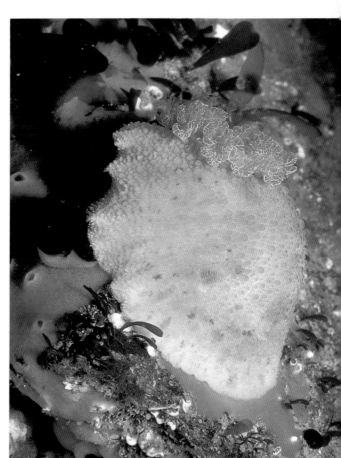

*Holothuria forskali*
Black Sea Cucumber or Cotton Spinner
*Súmaire cladaigh dubh*
(Photographer: Paul Kay)

**Left:** *Nucella lapillus* - Dogwhelk - *Cuachma chon*

Dogwhelks regularly feed on barnacles. They are the most dominant predators on the rocky shore.

(Photographer: Paul Kay)

**Right:** *Semibalanus balanoides*

Acorn Barnacle

*Garbhán carraige*

The acorn barnacle is common on the middle and lower shore.

(Photographer: Paul Kay)

**Below:** The dogwhelk lays its eggs deep in crevices in early summer.

(Photographer: Paul Kay)

*Tubularia indivisa* - Hydroid - *Hiodróideach*

These are sometimes found in vast quantities as a carpet on
rocks under water.

(Photographer: Keith Hiscock)

**Left:** *Chorda filum* - Bootlace Weed - *Ruálach*

Bootlace weed can grow up to 4.5 metres in length.

(Photographer: Paul Kay)

**Below:** *Lepidochitona cinereus* - Coat-of-mail - *Ciotón*

This mollusc has a shell of interlocking plates which allows it to roll up into a ball when threatened.

(Photographer: Paul Kay)

**Above:** *Ensis siliqua*
Razorshell "keyhole"
*Scian mhara*

Normally this is the only part of the razorshell that can be seen. Water is pumped through the "keyhole" to enable it to breathe and feed.

(Photographer: Paul Kay)

*Luidia ciliaris* - Seven-armed Starfish - *Na seacht méara*

All starfish can regenerate their limbs leading to individuals with varying arm lengths.

(Photographer: Paul Kay)

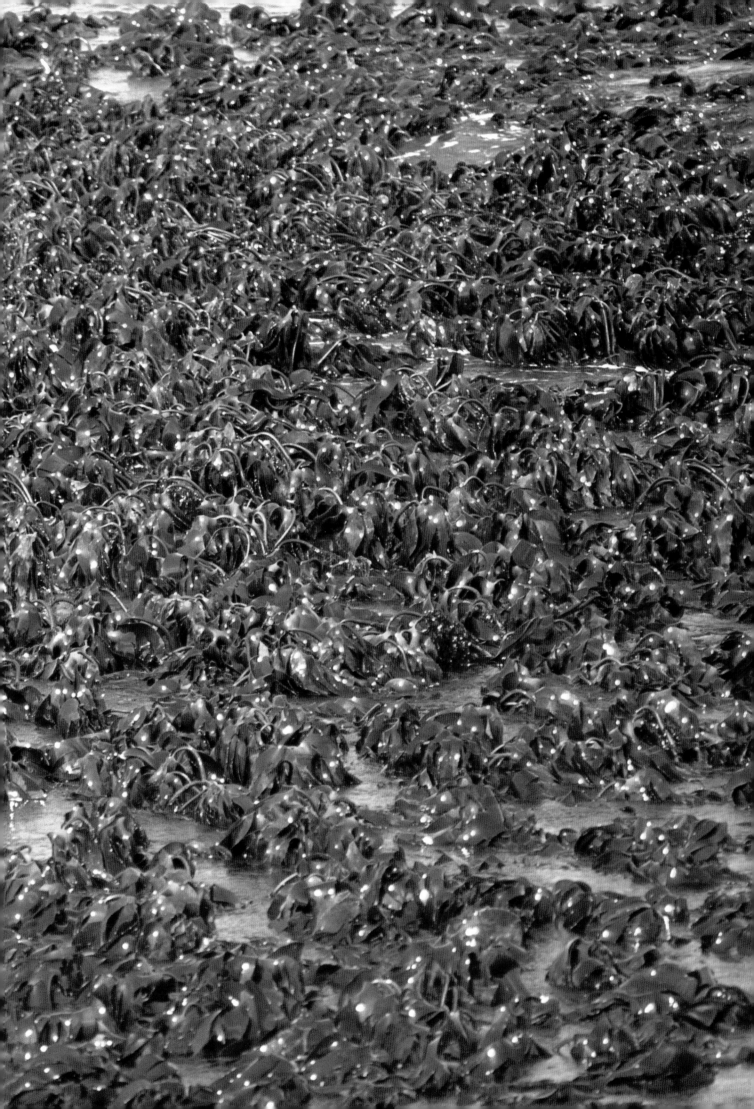

**Previous page:**  *Laminaria digitata* - Kelp - *Ceilp*

An exposed kelp forest.

(Photographer: Paul Kay)

**Above:**  The sea cucumber is found under rocks and in crevices with just the black tentacles exposed.

(Photographer: Paul Kay)

**Right:**  *Pawsonia saxicola*
Sea Cucumber
*Súmaire cladaigh*

The sea cucumber filters the water with its tentacles.

(Photographer: Paul Kay)

**Above:** *Echinus esculentus*
Common Sea-urchin
*Cuán mara*

(Photographer: Paul Kay)

**Right:** Sea-urchins are equipped with
very sharp spines for defence and
small nippers for grooming
themselves.

(Photographer: Paul Kay)

**Previous page:** *Actinothoë sphyrodeta*
*(Bundún leice)*

These delicate
anemones can be found
at a variety of coastal
habitats from rocky
outcrops to sheltered
harbours.

(Photographer: Paul Kay)

**Above:** The edible crab's shell looks like an old-fashioned piecrust.

(Photographer: Paul Kay)

**Left:** *Cancer pagurus* - Edible Crab - *Portán dearg*

When disturbed edible crabs will wedge themselves into crevices rather than try to escape.

(Photographer: Paul Kay)

**Above:** *Crossaster papposus* - Common Sun Star - *Crosóg ghréine*

(Photographer: Pete Atkinson)

**Right:** *Metridium senile* - Plumose Anemone - *Bláth mara*

(Photographer: Paul Kay)

A glorious autumn sunset.

(Photographer: Paul Kay)

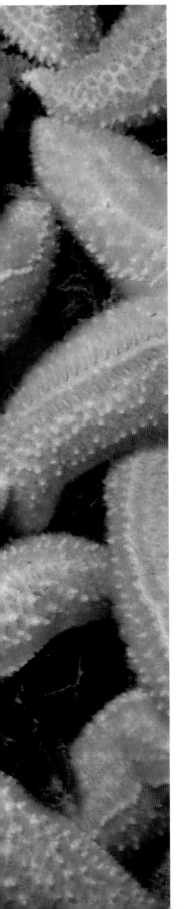

**Above:** *Mytilus edulis* - Common Mussel - *Diúilicín*

*Taurulus bubalis* - Long-spined Sea-scorpion - *Scairpiasc*

The long-spined sea-scorpion is well camouflaged on the mussel bed. These fish stay motionless for long periods of time in order to ambush unsuspecting prey.

(Photographer: Paul Kay)

**Left:** *Asterias rubens* - Common Starfish - *Crosóg mhara*

The common starfish is often found feeding on mussel beds.

(Photographer: Paul Kay)

73

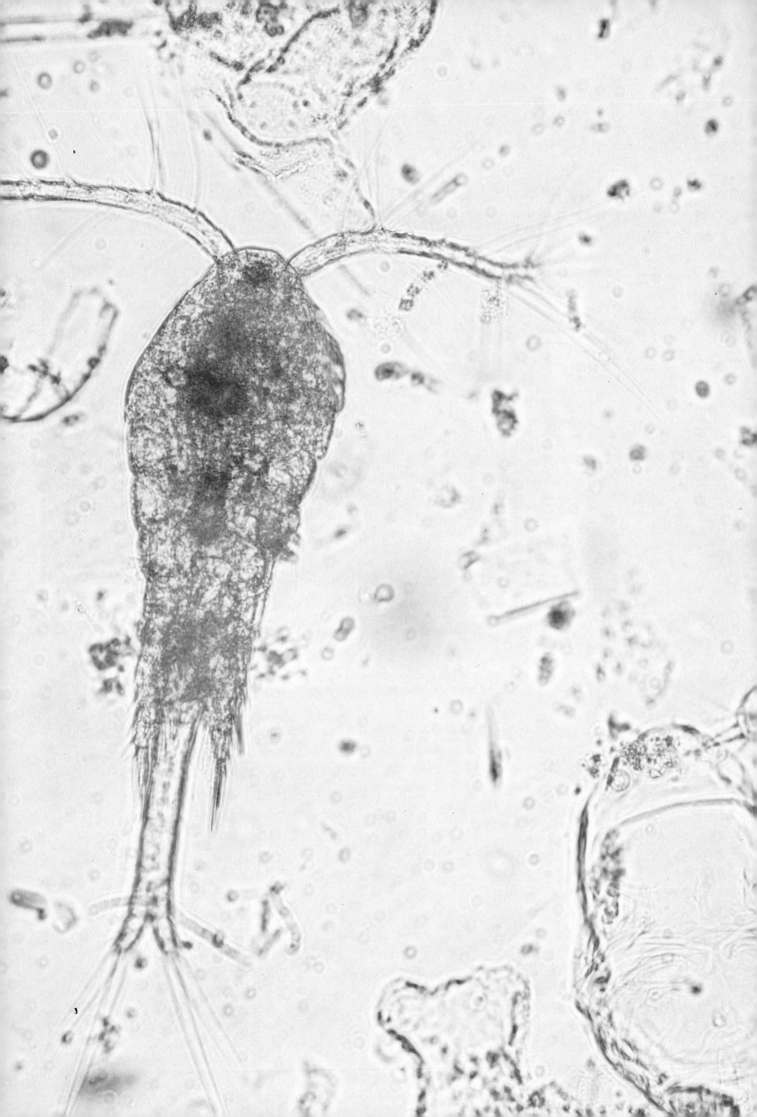

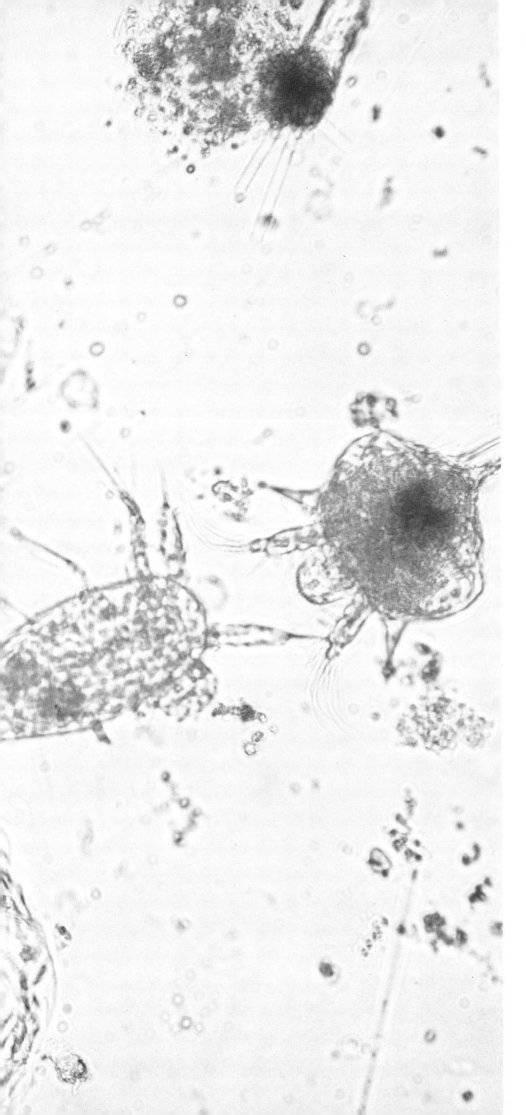

**Left:** Zooplankton - *Zóplanctón*

Zooplankton are microscopic animals that live throughout the sea.

(Photographer: Paul Kay)

**Above:**  *Asterias rubens* - Common Starfish - *Crosóg mhara*

This is the most likely starfish to be found on the beach.

(Photographer: Paul Kay)

**Opposite page:**  *Antedon bifida* - Feather-stars - *Crosóg chleiteach*

Feather-stars are aptly named.

(Photographer: Paul Kay)

**Right:** The arms of the starfish are covered with tube-feet which are used in feeding and moving.  This starfish is re-growing a limb

(Photographer: Paul Kay)

*Laminaria digitata* - Kelp - *Ceilp*

A kelp forest under water.

(Photographer: Paul Kay)

*Galathea intermedia* - Squat Lobster - *(Gliomach)*

(Photographer: Paul Kay)

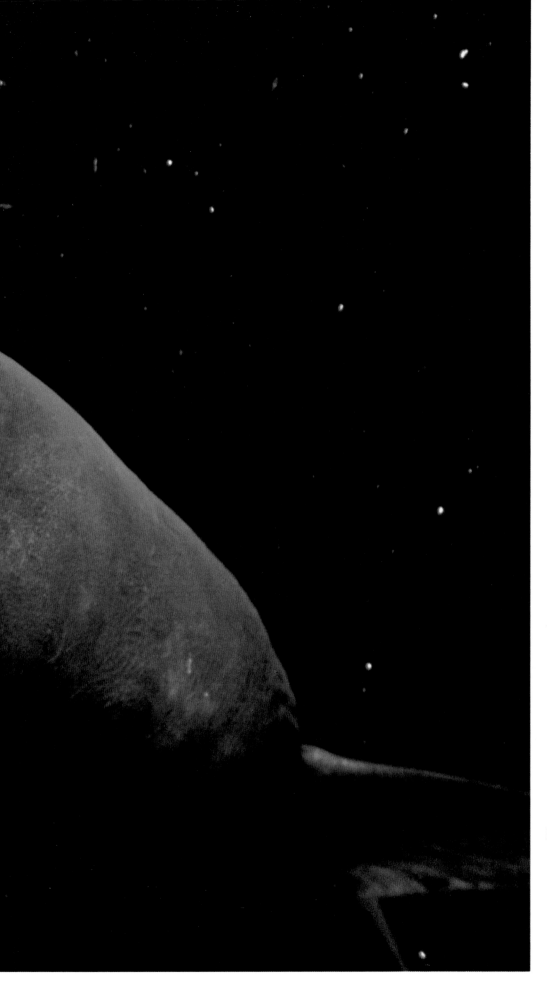

**Left:** *Conger conger*
Conger Eel
*Eascann choncair*

The conger eel tends to spend most of its time lurking in cracks and crevices.

(Photographer: Paul Kay)

**Below:** *Thorogobius ephippiatus* - Leopard-spot Goby - *Mac siobháin breac*

The leopard-spot goby is regularly found in holes and crevices. The characteristic blotches of red-brown pigment on its back give this goby its name.

(Photographer: Paul Kay)

**Above:** *Callionymus lyra*
Dragonet
*lascán nimhe*

The dragonet is a bottom living fish, with typically large dorsal eyes.

(Photographer: Paul Kay)

**Right:** *Littorina littoralis*
Flat Periwinkle
*Faocha leathan*

*Fucus sp.*
Wrack
*Casfheamainn*

This flat periwinkle is grazing on the wrack.

(Photographer: Paul Kay)

*Velella velella* - By-the-wind-sailor

By-the-wind-sailors are found in shoals on the Atlantic and
are often stranded in large numbers on beaches.

(Photographer: Paul Kay)

*Metridium senile* - Plumose Anemone - *Blátrmhara*
*Ophiothrix fragilis* - Brittle-star - *Crosóg bhriosc*

Plumose anemones on a brittle-star bed.

(Photographer: Paul Kay)

**Above:** *Pelvetia canaliculata* - Channel Wrack - *Caisíneach*

*Verrucaria maura* - Black Lichen - *Léicean dubh*

Channel wrack forms a very distinct narrow band along the top of the seashore. It has special water retaining capabilities.

(Photographer: Paul Kay)

**Opposite page:** Rockpool

An oasis of life in an otherwise harsh environment.

(Photographer: Paul Kay)

**Left:** Sponge
*(Spúinse)*

*Botryllusschlosseri*
Star Sea Squirt
*Ascaid réaltach*

The underside of rocks are often covered in encrusting sponges and sea squirts.

(Photographer: Paul Kay)

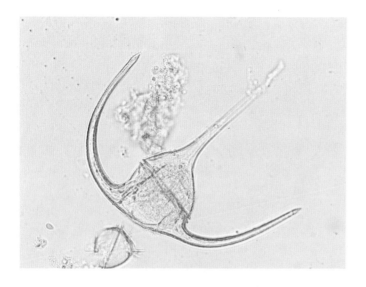

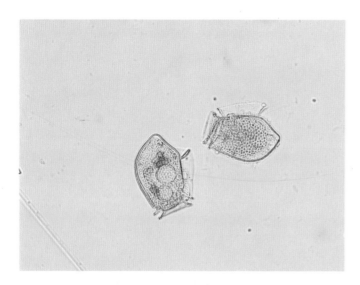

**Top:** *Ceratium tripos*

The whole sea depends on the microscopic phytoplankton that live in it. They are the beginning of the food chain.

(Photographer: Paul Kay)

**Above:** *Dinophysis acuta*

This species of phytoplankton commonly causes toxicity in shellfish.

(Photographer: Paul Kay)

**Right:** *Spirorbis sp.* - Encrusting Worm - *(Péist)*

The shells of the tube worms can occur in large numbers on animals, plants or rocks.

(Photographer: Paul Kay)

**Left:** *Suberites domuncula*
Sulphur Sponge
*(Spúinse)*

This is known as sulphur sponge when yellow and sea orange when orange. When disturbed this sponge will contract.

(Photographer: Paul Kay)

**Below:** *Inachus dorsettensis* - Scorpion Spider Crab - *Portán faoilinne*
*Suberties domuncula* - Sea Orange - *(Spúinse)*
*Ascidiella aspersa* - Sea Squirt - *Ascaid*

(Photographer: Paul Kay)

**Above:** *Centrolabrus rupestris* - Goldsinny Wrasse - *Ballach buí*

The goldsinny wrasse is commonly found in kelp. It is now being used in some fish farms to control lice on salmon.

(Photographer: Paul Kay)

**Below:** *Blennius gattorugine*
Tompot Blenny
*Ceannruán rocach*

The tompot blenny is characterised by its distinctive top knot.

(Photographer: Paul Kay)

**Overleaf:** *Urticina felina*
Dahlia Anemone
*Bundún leice dáilia*

(Photographer: Paul Kay)

**Right:** *Ophiothrix fragilis*
Brittle-star
*Crosóg bhriosc*

*Cliona celata*
Boring Sponge
*(Spúinse)*

Boring sponge forms a back drop to the brittle-star which are sometimes found in millions.

(Photographer: Paul Kay)

**Below:** *Cliona celata* - Boring Sponge - *(Spúinse)*

Whilst most of the sponges are hard to identify this one, in its massive form, is hard to mistake as it is always big and yellow.

(Photographer: Paul Kay)

**Above:** *Porcellana platycheles* - Broad-clawed Porcelain Crab - *(Portán poircealláin)*
The broad-clawed porcelain crab can be found under stones in muddy areas.
(Photographer: Paul Kay)

**Below:** *Macropipus depurator*
Swimming Crab
*Luaineachán*

This Crab is very common in shallow Water

(Photographer: Paul Kay)

**Left:** *Echinus esculentus*
Common Sea-urchin
*Cuán mara*

*Alcyonium digitatum*
Dead Man's Fingers
*Méara mara*

*Actinothoë clavata*
(Bundún leice)

(Photographer: Paul Kay)

*Cancer pagurus* - Edible Crab - *Portán dearg*

(Photographer: Paul Kay)

**Below:** *Scyliorhinus canicula* - Lesser-spotted Dogfish - *Fíogach beag*

The lesser-spotted dogfish has a very heightened sense of smell.

(Photographer: Paul Kay)

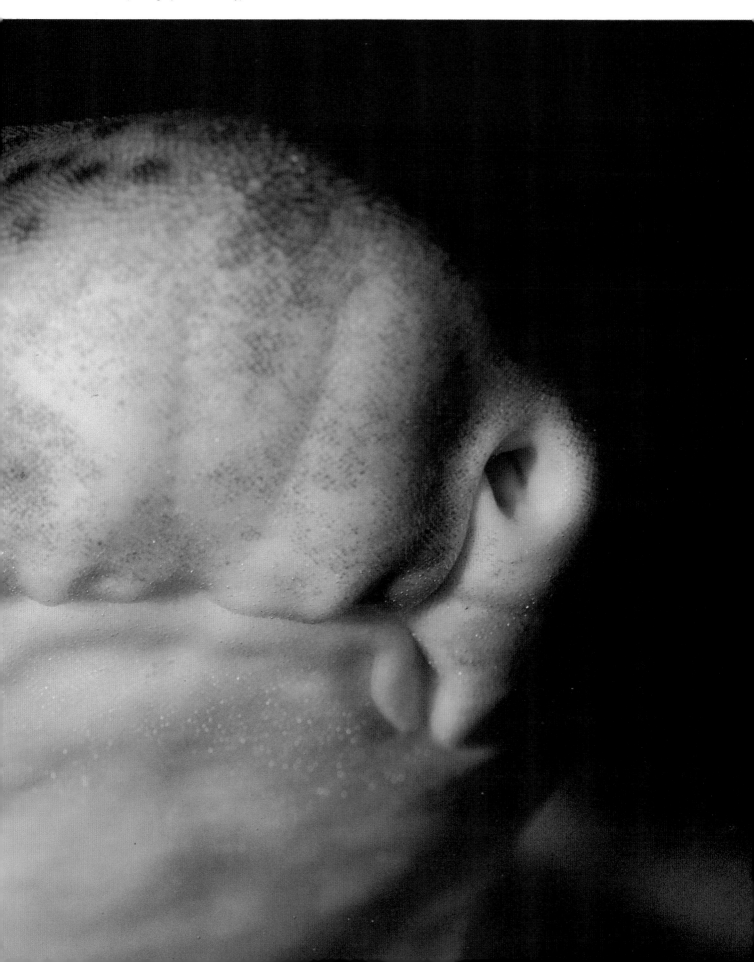

**Above:** *Octopus vulgaris* - Common Octopus - *Ochtapas*

(Photographer: Paul Kay)

**Left:** *Sertularia* - Sea Fir - *Giúis mhara*

Sea firs have a plant-like appearance but are in fact a multitude of animals.

(Photographer: Paul Kay)

**Below:** *Haliclystus auricula* - Sessile or Stalked Jellyfish
*Smugairle róin neamhghasánach*

These peculiar jellyfish are found attached to seaweed in rockpools or shallow water.

(Photographer: Paul Kay)

**Left:** *Pholis gunnellus*

Butterfish

*Sleamhnóg*

Butterfish are found under rocks on the shore and are very slippery.

(Photographer: Paul Kay)

**Left:** *Pleuronectes platessa* - Plaice - *Leathóg bhallach*

Plaice can usually be recognised by their orange dots.

(Photographer: Paul Kay)

**Below:** *Labrus bergylta* - Ballan Wrasse - *Ballach breac*

The ballan wrasse uses algae to build a nest in crevices.

(Photographer: Paul Kay)

**Above:** *Clavelina lepadiformis* - Light-bulb Sea Squirt - *(Ascaid)*
*Prostheceraeus vittatus* - Candy-stripe Flatworm - *(Leithphéist)*
The candy-stripe flatworm is often found on the light-bulb sea squirt.

(Photographer: Paul Kay)

**Right:** *Echinus esculentus*
Common Sea-urchin
*Cuán mara*

(Photographer: Pete Atkinson)

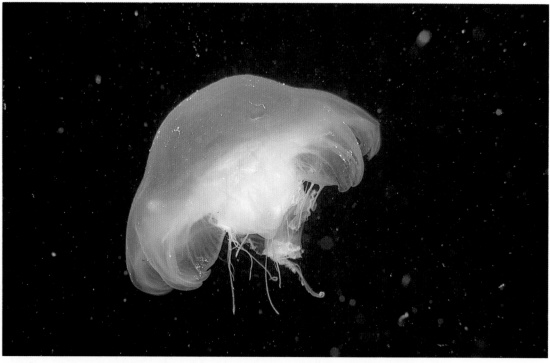

**Above:** *Cyanea lamarckii* - Stinging Jellyfish - *Smugairle róin nimhe*
This is one of the few jellyfish in Irish waters that can inflict stings.

(Photographer: Paul Kay)

*Patina pellucida* - Blue-rayed Limpets - *Bairneach mín*

*Membranipora membranacea* - Sea Mat - *Milseán mara*

The blue-rayed limpets feed on the kelp whilst the sea mat filters the surrounding water.

(Photographer: Paul Kay)

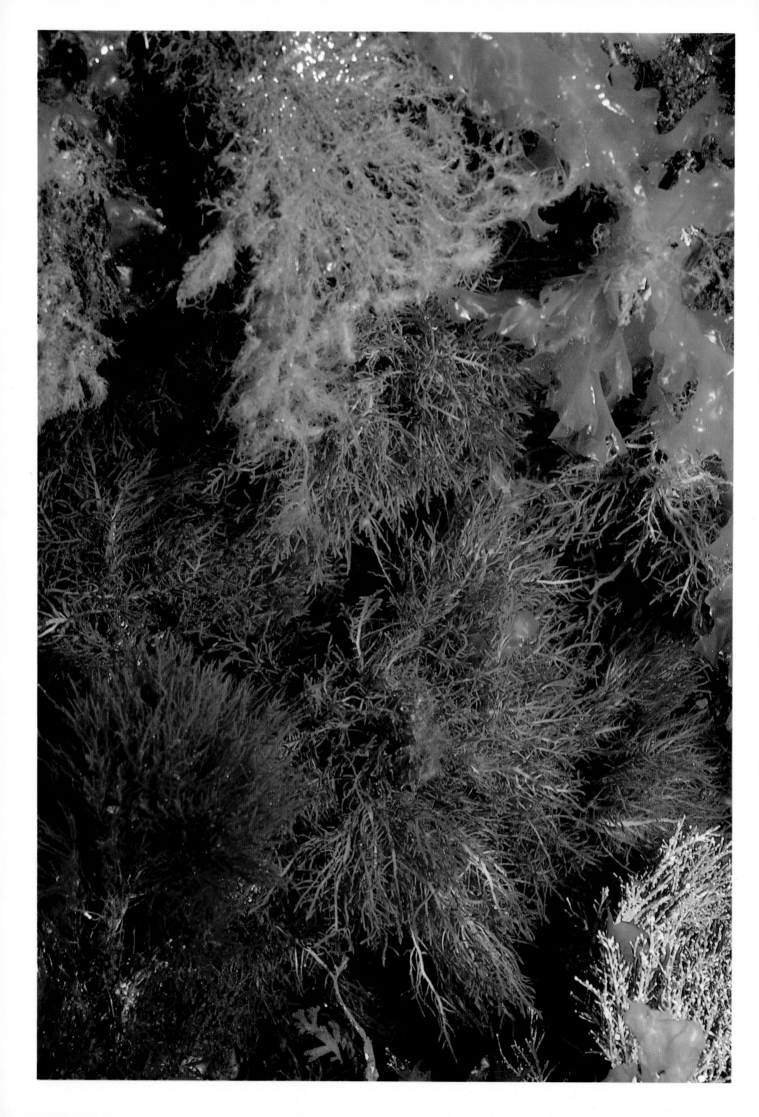

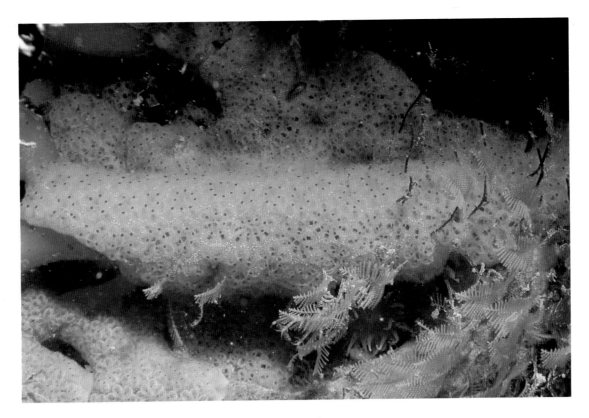

**Above:** *Botryllus schlosseri* - Star Sea Squirt - *Ascaid réaltach*

Star sea squirt form distinctive circular groups or stars on seaweeds and rocks on the lower shore and shallow water.

(Photographer: Paul Kay)

**Below:** *Botryllus schlosseri* - Star Sea Squirt - *Ascaid réaltach*

*Fucus serratus* - Toothed Wrack - *Míoránach*

(Photographer: Paul Kay)

**Left:** *Henricia oculata* - Bloody Henry - *(Crosóg)*
This starfish is most commonly found in exposed areas.

(Photographer: Paul Kay)

**Right:** *Polycera quadrilineata*
Sea Slug
*Bodalach*

Sea slugs come in varied colours, in some cases almost fluorescent.

(Photographer: Paul Kay)

**Overleaf:** *Homarus gammarus* - Lobster - *Gliomach*
The young lobster excavates a hiding place under rocks for protection.

(Photographer: Paul Kay)

**Below:** Behind the sea slugs can be seen the wealth of life that is typical of underwater rock faces.

(Photographer: Paul Kay)

**Top:** *Syngnathus acus* - Greater Pipefish - *Snáthaidmhara*

The pipefish is often found amongst seaweed - in this case *Chondrus crispus.*

(Photographer: Paul Kay)


**Above:** The head of the greater pipefish. After fertilization the female pipefish passes on the eggs to the male, who in turn broods on them until they escape from the brood pouch.

(Photographer: Paul Kay)


**Left:** *Nerophis lumbriciformis* - Worm Pipefish - Pis an ribe
*Flustra foliacea* - Hornwrack - *Teanga chait*

(Photographer: Paul Kay)

**Above:** *Agonus cataphractus* - Pogge or Armed Bullhead - *Muiricín*

The pogge has a distinctive fleshy beard.

(Photographer: Paul Kay)

**Left:** *Ascidiella aspersa*
Sea Squirt
*Ascaid*

In order to feed and breathe, water is sucked in through the top hole and out through the bottom hole.

(Photographer: Paul Kay)

**Below:** *Pollachius pollachius* - Pollack - *Mangach*

Pollack is a member of the cod family and swims in shoals.

(Photographer: Paul Kay)

**Above:** *Balistes carolinensis* - Triggerfish

The triggerfish has very strong jaws that are capable of tearing a crab to bits.

(Photographer: Paul Kay)

**Below:** *Carcinus maenas* - Common Shore Crab - *Portán glas*

The common shore crab can be found quite high on the seashore and can tolerate long periods out of water.

(Photographer: Paul Kay)

**Right:** Caprella linearis
Ghost Shrimp
*(Séacla)*

This ghost shrimp is no more than 5mm in height.

(Photographer: Paul Kay)

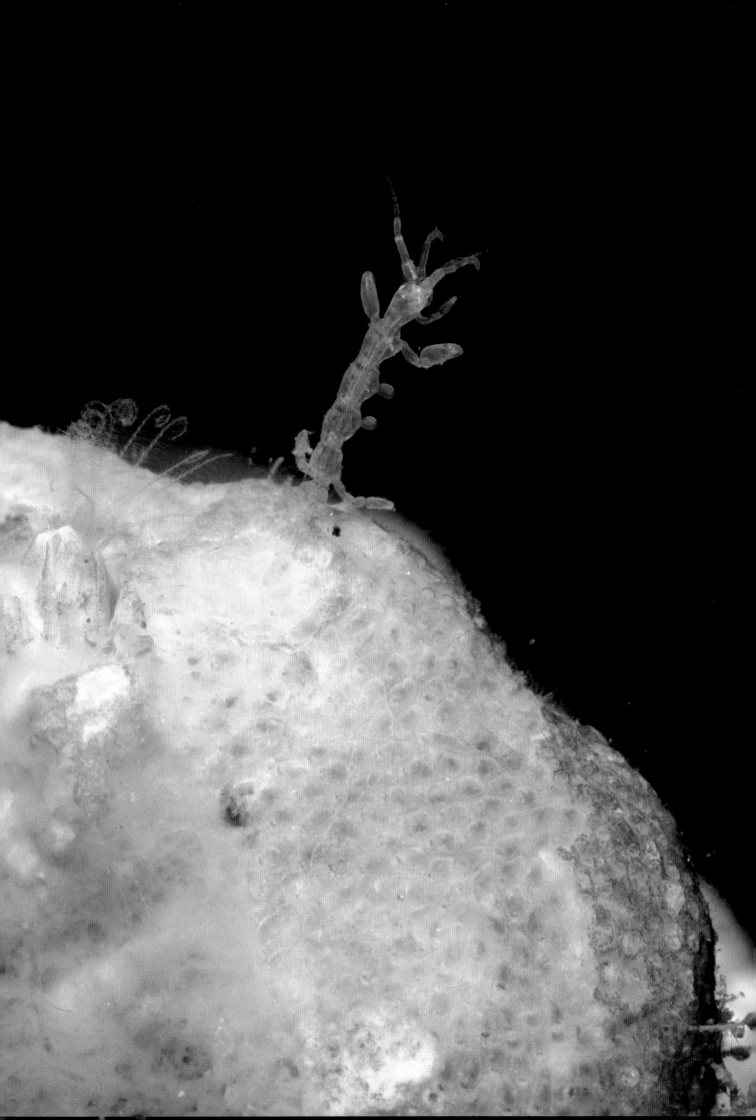

**Above:** *Macropipus puber*
Velvet Swimming Crab
*Luaineachán mín*

A male will clasp on to a female to
protect her prior to mating.

(Photographer: Paul Kay)

**Right:** Velvet swimming crabs are easily
recognised by their brilliant red eyes
and blue claws.

(Photographer: Paul Kay)

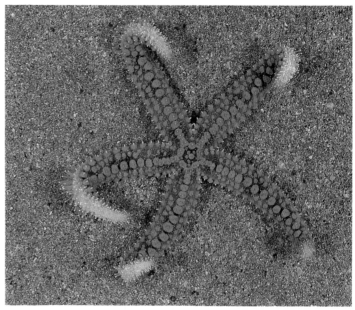

**Above:** *Marthasterias glacialis*
Spiny Starfish
*Crosóg choilgneach*

The spiny starfish can grow to over 50cm in diameter when adult.

(Photographer: Paul Kay)

**Left:** *Ophiothrix fragilis* - Brittle-star - *Crosóg bhriosc*

A close-up of the common brittle-star.

(Photographer: Paul Kay)

*Laminaria digitata* - Kelp - *Ceilp*

Low spring tides expose the tip of the kelp forest.

(Photographer: Paul Kay)

*Calliostoma  zizyphinum* - Painted Topshell - *Faochán Muire dathannach*

This painted topshell is grazing on bryozoan *Umbonula sp*.

(Photographer: Paul Kay)

**Left:** *Cereus pedunculatus* - Daisy Anemone - (Bundún leice)

This daisy anemone has attached itself to an empty oyster shell.

(Photographer: Paul Kay)

**Below:** The light filtering through the water distorts, making everything seem bigger to the diver.

(Photographer: Paul Kay)

**Above:** *Pomatoceros triqueter* - Encrusting Worm - *(Péist)*

A tube worm produces a hard ridged chalky shell inside which it lives.

(Photographer: Paul Kay)

**Right:** *Sabella pavonina* - Peacock Worm

The peacock worm uses its fan to filter the water for food.

(Photographer: Paul Kay)

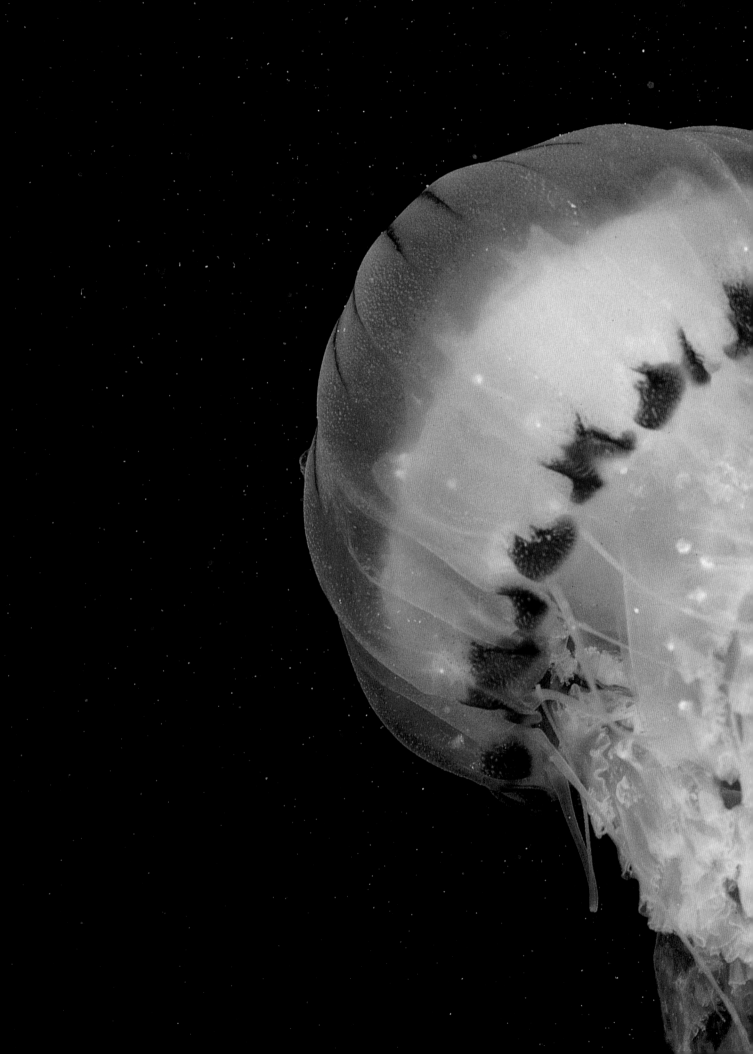

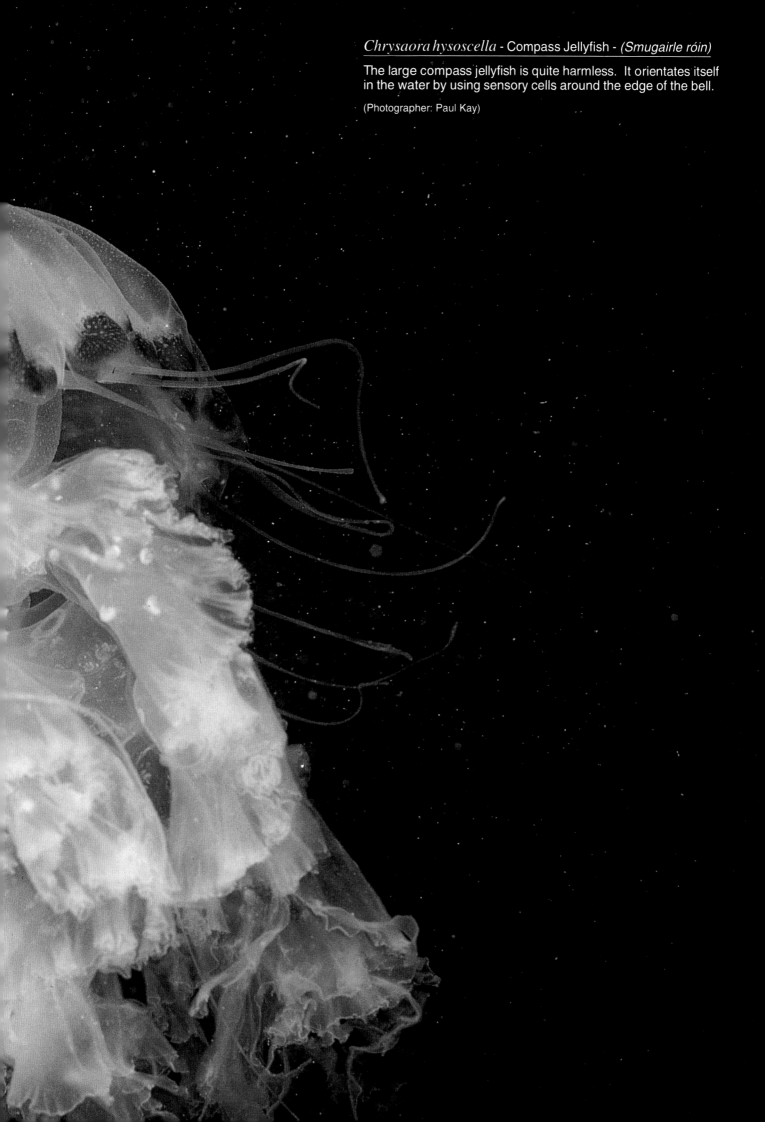

*Chrysaora hysoscella* - Compass Jellyfish - *(Smugairle róin)*

The large compass jellyfish is quite harmless. It orientates itself in the water by using sensory cells around the edge of the bell.

(Photographer: Paul Kay)

**Left:** *Pholis gunnellus*
Butterfish
*Sleamhnóg*

(Photographer: Paul Kay)

**Above:** *Psammechinus miliaris* - Green Sea-urchin - *Cuán mara glas*

This sea-urchin is particularly hard to find as it is inclined to hide itself with gravel, shell, weed or other debris.

(Photographer: Paul Kay)

**Below:** *Asterina gibbosa* - Cushion-star - *Crosóg faoileáin*

Cushion-stars rarely grow more than 5cm in diameter.

(Photographer: Paul Kay)

**Right:** *Sagartia elegans* var. *rosea*
*(Bundún leice)*

This anemone often occurs in large groups and is typified by its rose red tentacles.

(Photographer: Paul Kay)

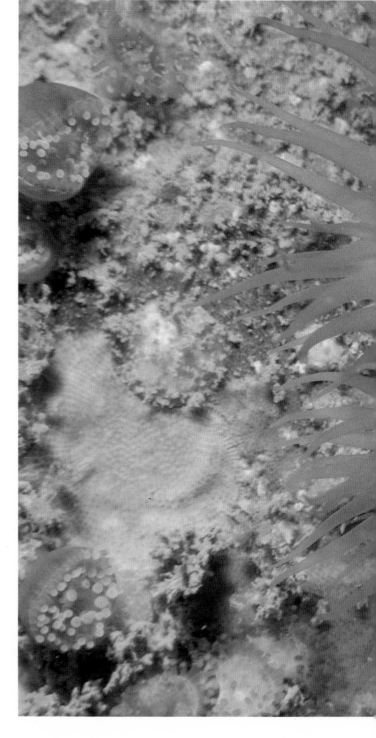

**Above:** *Urticina felina* - Dahlia Anemone - *Bundún leice dáilia*

(Photographer: Paul Kay)

144

**Right:** *Bunodactis verrucosa*
Gem Anemone
*(Bundún leice)*

(Photographer: Paul Kay)

**Above:** *Neoturris pileata* - Medusa - *Meadúsa*

This is a juvenile form of the adult Sea Fir.

(Photographer: Steve Weinberg)

**Opposite page:** *Doto fragilis* - Sea Slug - *Bodalach*

This walnut-like sea slug feeds on hydroids and can be found in shallow waters.

(Photographer: Paul Kay)

**Below:** *Crangon vulgaris*
Common Shrimp
*Séacla*

(Photographer: Paul Kay)

**Right:** *Littorina saxatilis*
Rough Periwinkle
*Faocha gharbh*

Their grooved shells come in a mixture of colours and patterns.

(Photographer: Paul Kay)

**Below:** *Nassarius incrassatus*
Netted Dogwhelk
*(Cuachma chon)*

This netted dogwhelk's shell has been well worn.

(Photographer: Paul Kay)

**Overleaf:** *Corynactis viridis* - Jewel Anemone - *(Bundún leice)*

These anemones come in a variety of colours and often in dense patches.

(Photographer: Paul Kay)

149

**Above:** *Homarus gammarus*
Lobster - *Gliomach*

Lobsters are blue and when cooked will turn red.

(Photographer: Paul Kay)

**Below:** *Xantho incisus - (Portán)*

These crabs often have disproportionately large claws.

(Photographer: Paul Kay)

**Right:** *Elminius modestus*
Darwin's Barnacle
*Giúrann Darwin*

Darwin's barnacle is an introduced species from Australia. It has rapidly spread throughout Northern Europe.

(Photographer: Paul Kay)

*Ophiothrix fragilis* - Brittle-star - *Crosóg bhriosc*

This young brittle-star is in the spines of a sea-urchin.

(Photographer: Paul Kay)

*Carcinus maenas* - Common Shore Crab - *Portán glas*

Shore crabs have violent natures and often fight amongst themselves.

(Photographer: Paul Kay)